Little Orphan Annie

VOL
 3

1933

BY HAROLD GRAY

VOL
3
1933

FANTAGRAPHICS BOOKS
7563 Lake City Way NE
Seattle, WA 98115

Edited by Gary Groth.
Design by Pat Moriarity.
Production by Mark Thompson.
Published by Gary Groth and Kim Thompson.
Color separations by Port Publications.

First Fantagraphics Books edition: October, 1991.
1 3 5 7 9 8 6 4 2

ISBN: 1-56097-039-1

Library of Congress Catalog Number: 84-81462.

Printed in the U.S.A.

HAROLD GRAY

Of Politics and Blank Orbs

By R.C. Harvey

Long celebrated as the first major comic strip to venture into political commentary, Harold Gray's *Little Orphan Annie* didn't begin to make overtly political statements until the 1930s when the strip was well into its second decade. But with this volume of the Fantagraphics *Little Orphan Annie* reprint series, we reach the eve of Gray's first forays into the arena of politics. Syndicated cartoonists traditionally avoided expressing views on such subjects because they were reasonably certain that their strips would be dropped by papers whose editors didn't agree with them, and they understandably didn't want to lose circulation. But when Franklin D. Roosevelt took office on March 4, 1933 (a few months after the strips in this volume began their initial run), the stage was set for a confrontation between Gray's conservatism and FDR's New Deal philosophy.

Oddly enough, *Little Orphan Annie* would reach the zenith of its popularity during the Depression '30s. "Odd" because it was FDR's decade, the age of the man who gave government a social conscience. And FDR's mission ran in directions diametrically opposed to Gray's ideas. Under Roosevelt's tutelage, the down-trodden and the poor, the halt and the lame were encouraged to

look to government for help rather than exhorted to help themselves by working hard and exercising diligently the principles of free enterprise. Gray's message was precisely the opposite—although it was as much an accident of his story as it was a matter of political conviction.

Gray didn't set out to write a political tract; he set out to tell a story about an orphan girl. As a good storyteller, Gray knew that the best way for a little orphan girl to make her way in the world without being simply a weepy milksop is for her to be triumphantly self-reliant. Annie's entourage was a natural outgrowth of this central notion. Within two months of the strip's debut, Gray had introduced the character who would shape this philosophy of independence into a political stance. Annie was adopted by Oliver "Daddy" Warbucks,

a millionaire industrialist, and Warbucks quickly became Gray's example of the self-made man, the self-reliant individualst who made himself what he is through purposeful enterprise. The epitome of this culture hero, Warbucks is the larger-than-life version of what all the "little people" in the strip inevitably become if they follow Annie's example of hard work and canny capitalism. As Gray's exemplar, Warbucks could scarcely espouse self-reliance and free enterprise during the Roosevelt years without, at the same time, attacking FDR's policies. And so *Little Orphan Annie* became the first comic strip to be unabashedly, unrelievedly, "political." But it did so because the very essence of its story demanded it.

Gray's own renowned conservatism was hardly negligible in the development of the strip's political thrust. But neither was the strip's political content artificially superimposed upon an otherwise simple tale of a wandering orphan girl and her dog. The strip's politics were organic, integral to its story and its heroine's personality.

Despite Gray's scathing assaults on the principles of the New Deal, the strip was enormously popular. Gray's mailbox testified to that. Every time he plunged Annie into a new dire predicament, letters from readers poured in to plead for mercy for the hapless waif. The sequence that opens this volume prompted a telegram from Dearborn, Michigan: "Please do all you can to help Annie find Sandy. Stop. We are all interested. Henry Ford."

A self-made individualist himself, Ford could be expected to share Gray's views. But what accounted for the strip's undeniable appeal to millions of the less fortunate during this time of national hardship?

The fact is that the strip spoke to most people in terms that addressed the most profound of their concerns in those economic hard times. The events of the Great Depression unfolded gradually: the world did not collapse overnight. And as the

THOSE DOG-GONED PICKPOCKETS MISSED A FEW DOLLARS, ENOUGH TO KEEP US GOIN' A COUPLE O' DAYS, OR SO- BUT THAT TRIP TO COSMIC CITY IS OFF, FOR NOW, AT LEAST-

12-6-33

economic institutions of the country crumbled one after another, the dominant emotion among the population was fear—fear that an entire way of life, the American way, was falling apart. Gray's strip addressed and assuaged that fear. Annie's adventures proved again and again that the historic American ethic of hard work was not bankrupt and that capitalism could still work. Readers were reassured and comforted.

Gray's graphic style was perfectly suited to the temper of the times. Annie's blank eyeballs, for instance—a much lampooned apsect of Gray's style—became integral to the mood of the strip in the fearful climate of the day. Although there was

little action in many of Gray's tales, Annie seemed perpetually immersed in a sinister word that threatened to assault her at every street corner, a world in which Phineas Pinchpennys always lurk in alleys with clubs to do her harm—a world that Gray would increasingly shroud with heavy black solids and darkly shaded nooks and crannies as his style matured in the mid-to-late '30s. And Annie's blank eyeballs were marvelously appropriate to her situation. One walks through a vaguely threatening world gingerly, never looking behind or to the side for fear of seeing a sinister presence there. One keeps his eyes focused rigidly ahead of him, in a kind of unseeing stare—precisely the effect that Annie's blank eyeballs evoke. (It would have been an inspired graphic touch had Gray invented the device expressly for this purpose. But he was only following one of the conventions of early comic strip art: George McManus drew Jiggs's and Maggie's eyes the same way in *Bringing Up Father*, where the effect produced was quite different. Still, Annie's unseeing stare unquestionably added to the ambiance of the strip.)

And Gray's treatment of the human figure created kindred feelings. His characters seem to posture woodenly, but this rigidity suggests that the people of Gray's sinister world are inhibited, restrained in their movement—perhaps because they are afraid. In effect, they seem virtually paralyzed with fear and apprehension. In such a world, we are not surprised when violence breaks out—when Phineas Pinchpenny tries to run Annie down with his car or when the Cosmic City citizens attack Pinchpenny and his son as they return after doing away with Annie. In such a world, violence belongs. We have been led to expect it.

Graphically and philosophically, Gray's strip was an integrated whole. His style and graphic conventions suited perfectly the vision of the world that he held. And his philosophy and his stories were a seamless tapestry. Few comic strips can claim similar accomplishments. Few begin with such complex ambitions. And of the few that do, fewer yet achieve them as fully—as artistically—as *Little Orphan Annie* did. ●

YOUR FIDDLE WAS TH' FIRST THING THAT CAME HANDY- GEE- I NEVER MEANT TO SMASH IT OVER THAT GUY'S HEAD-

I WAS GLAD YOU DID, ANNIE- IT WASN'T A VERY GOOD FIDDLE, ANYWAY-

2

4

5

6

RIGHT IN THERE, UNDER THAT BUSH, IS WHERE I FOUND SANDY- AND THERE WERE NO TRACKS AND IT HADN'T SNOWED, SINCE HE DISAPPEARED-

1-19-33

THAT MEANS HE WAS TOSSED IN THERE- DOC. SAYS AN AUTO MUST HAVE HIT HIM- ALMOST EVERY BONE IN HIS BODY WAS BUSTED- BUT, EVEN SO, IT COULDN'T HAVE KNOCKED HIM CLEAR OVER THIS FENCE-

AH, HERE WE ARE- TRACKS CLEAR UP ONTO THE SIDE WALK- WHO EVER IT WAS MUST HAVE MEANT TO HIT HIM- AND THIS IS 'MOST A BLOCK FROM WHERE I FOUND HIM-

AND HERE'S A DROP OF BLOOD, STILL ON THIS FENCE- I GET IT, NOW- HE WAS HIT HERE, AND, WHOEVER IT WAS, CARRIED HIM AWAY FROM HERE AND TOSSED HIM INTO THAT BUSH, FOR DEAD-

HAROLD GRAY

Reg. U. S. Pat. Off., Copyright, 1933, by The Chicago Tribune

OH, YOU'RE MISS SWEET, ANNIE'S TEACHER- WON'T YOU COME IN?

THANK YOU, MRS. FUTILE- I JUST COULDN'T HELP CALLING, TO SEE HOW SANDY IS- AND, OF COURSE, I WANT TO SEE ANNIE, TOO-

I'M AFRAID ANNIE SHOULDN'T HAVE STAYED OUT OF SCHOOL-

NOT AT ALL- I UNDERSTAND IT, PERFECTLY- WHY, ANYWAY, SHE'S THE BRIGHTEST SCHOLAR IN HER CLASS- SHE'LL CATCH UP IN NO TIME-

1-20-33

OH, THE POOR CHAP- WAS HE STRUCK BY A CAR, ANNIE?

YES, MISS SWEET, HE WAS- AND THEN HE WAS CARRIED A BLOCK AND HIDDEN IN A BUSH-

OH, WHO ON EARTH COULD HAVE DONE SUCH A CRUEL THING?

THAT'S SOMETHIN' I AIM TO FIND OUT, MISS SWEET- I CERTAINLY DO-

HAROLD GRAY

OH, SANDY, YOU MUST PULL THROUGH- YOU'VE JUST GOT TO BEAT IT, SANDY- YOU CAN'T SEE ME, AND YOU CAN'T MOVE, BUT YOU CAN HEAR ME, MAYBE- AND YOU KNOW HOW MUCH I CARE, SANDY- YOU'VE GOT TO LIVE-

1-21-33

WHY, SANDY AND I HAVE BEEN TO-GETHER, ALMOST FROM THE FIRST- HE WAS JUST A LITTLE PUPPY, WHEN I FOUND HIM IN THE ALLEY THAT DAY, BACK OF MRS. BOTTLE'S STORE- GEE, THAT WAS A LONG TIME AGO-

WE'VE BEEN THROUGH A HEAP TO-GETHER, SANDY- GOOD TIMES AND BAD TIMES- BUT HAVIN' YOU HAS MADE THE BAD TIMES EASIER AND THE GOOD TIMES BETTER-

AND SANDY- NO MATTER WHAT HAPPENS, I SWEAR I'LL SQUARE THIS THING- YOU CAN COUNT ON ME- BUT, SANDY- FIGHT NOW, AS YOU NEVER FOUGHT BEFORE- I CAN'T LOSE YOU, SANDY- I CAN'T- I CAN'T

HAROLD GRAY Reg. U. S. Pat. Off., Copyright, 1933, by The Chicago Tribune

OF COURSE, IF IT WAS SOME ORDINARY THING, IT'D BE DIFFERENT- BUT THIS IS SERIOUS-

1-26-33

I CAN'T TAKE ANY CHANCES O' PICKIN' TH' WRONG BIRD- JUST CAUSE I DON'T LIKE SOMEBODY, IS NO REASON TO SAY HE DID IT-

I'VE GOT TO HAVE PROOF- REAL PROOF- I'VE BEEN OVER EVERY INCH O' THIS BLOCK- THERE'S TH' AUTO TRACKS AND SANDY'S BLOOD- BUT NOTHIN' ELSE-

Reg. U.S. Pat. Off.; Copyright, 1933, by The Chicago Tribune.

NOT A WITNESS- NOT A LOST BUTTON, OR A PIECE O' TORN COAT, ON A NAIL- NOTHIN'- BUT THAT'S O.K.- IT'S NOT BRAINS THAT COUNT SO MUCH IN CATCHIN' CRIMINALS- IT'S SEEIN' EVERY THING AND NEVER GIVING UP-

HAROLD GRAY

NO, SIR, MR. AGATE- SO FAR I HAVEN'T FOUND OUT A THING, TO PROVE WHO IT WAS HIT SANDY-

WELL, I'M COUNTING ON YOU, ANNIE- SOME DAY YOU'LL FIND OUT- BUT WHEN YOU DO, WHAT THEN? WHAT DO YOU PLAN ON DOING TO WHOEVER IT IS?

1-27-33

OH, I HAVEN'T FIGGERED THAT FAR YET- BUT EVEN IF I DID KNOW WHAT I'D DO TO WHOEVER IT WAS, I WOULDN'T TELL-

YOU WOULDN'T TELL? WHY NOT, ANNIE?

WELL, YOU SEE, MR. AGATE, I FIGGER IF YOU'RE GOIN' TO DO SOMETHIN' TO SOME BIRD, AND YOU TALK ABOUT IT, YOU WARN HIM- AND WHY WARN A GUY LIKE THAT, SO HE'LL KNOW WHAT TO LOOK OUT FOR?

HM-M- SAY, THAT'S NOT BAD LOGIC-

IN FACT, IT'S DOGGONED GOOD LOGIC- MY BET IS THAT LITTLE TYKE WILL CATCH UP WITH WHOEVER NEARLY KILLED HER DOG- YES, AND WHEN SHE DOES, I'LL BET THE PAY-OFF WILL BE LIKE A BOLT OF LIGHTNING-

Reg. U.S. Pat. Off.; Copyright, 1933, by The Chicago Tribune.

HAROLD GRAY

I SEE YOU'VE BEEN FIXIN' UP AN AUTO BUMPER- WHAT WAS TH' MATTER WITH IT, MR. FORGE?

OH, YES, ANNIE- ELMER PINCHPENNY'S CAR- RAN INTO THE GARAGE DOOR ABOUT A WEEK AGO, I UNDERSTAND- IT WASN'T BROKEN- JUST BENT-

1-28-33

NOT GOING TO LEAVE ME ALL ALONE HERE SO SOON, ARE YOU, ANNIE?

OH, I JUST DROPPED IN TO SAY HELLO- I'VE GOT TO GET BACK TO THE STORE, SO MR. FUTILE CAN GO HOME TO DINNER- SO LONG, MR. FORGE-

HAIR! REDDISH, SANDY COLORED HAIR- AND IT WAS CAUGHT ON A BOLT ON ELMER PINCHPENNY'S CAR BUMPER, AND TH' BUMPER WAS BENT A WEEK AGO-

COURSE, IT MIGHT NOT BE SANDY'S HAIR- AND MAYBE SOMEBODY ELSE WAS DRIVIN' HIS CAR, THAT NIGHT- JUST THE SAME, THIS LOOKS LIKE A CLEW, BUT I'M NOT PEDDLIN' A WORD ABOUT THIS TO ANYBODY- NOT EVEN TO SANDY, YET-

Reg. U.S. Pat. Off.; Copyright, 1933, by The Chicago Tribune.

HAROLD GRAY

Little Orphan Annie

YUH CAN'T TELL MUCH, JUST BY LOOKIN' AT A LITTLE TUFT O' HAIR—

COURSE IT LOOKS LIKE TH' SAME KIND O' HAIR SANDY WEARS— BUT THAT DOESN'T PROVE A THING— MAYBE IT ISN'T EVEN DOG HAIR—

SOUND ASLEEP— POOR OLD FELLOW— HE'S STILL A MIGHTY SICK DOG— BUT DOC. SAYS HE'LL GET WELL, IF HE DOESN'T HAVE A RELAPSE—

EASY, NOW— ALL I NEED IS JUST A SAMPLE— NO NEED O' WAKIN' SANDY, IF I'M REAL CAREFUL—

THERE— THAT SURE LOOKS JUST TH' SAME AS TH' HAIR I FOUND ON THAT AUTO BUMPER— FUNNY ABOUT THAT— I JUST HAPPENED TO DROP INTO TH' BLACK-SMITH SHOP—

AND THERE WAS ELMER PINCHPENNY'S AUTO BUMPER, BEIN' FIXED— AND THERE WAS A LITTLE TUFT O' HAIR CAUGHT ON ONE O' TH' BOLTS—

NOBODY NOTICED, WHEN I TOOK THOSE FEW WISPS O' HAIR AND WALKED OUT— AND NOW HERE THEY ARE, ON THIS PAPER— AND ON THIS PAPER ARE SOME HAIRS FROM SANDY—

WELL, THEY LOOK JUST ALIKE TO ME— SAME COLOR AND EVER'THING— BUT I'M NO EXPERT— I'M GOIN' TO BE SURE 'BOUT THIS—

IF I CAN PROVE THAT THE HAIR ON THAT BUMPER CAME OFF O' SANDY, I'LL KNOW WHO 'TWAS RAN HIM DOWN AND 'MOST KILLED HIM—

BUT EVEN IF I PROVE THAT, THERE'S NO LAW TO PUNISH HIM— WHAT SQUARIN' IS DONE, I'LL DO— SO I'M KEEPIN' MY MOUTH SHUT—

DOC'S GOT A MIKER-SCOPE— HE CAN TELL 'BOUT THIS HAIR— BUT I DON'T HAVE TO TELL HIM WHY I WANT TO KNOW— NOPE— THIS IS ALL MY JOB—

AND, BELIEVE ME, IF I'M ON TH' RIGHT TRAIL, I WON'T NEED ANY HELP TO SQUARE WHAT HE DID TO SANDY—

HAROLD GRAY

Reg. U.S. Pat. Off. Copyright, 1933, by The Chicago Tribune.

13

17

19

23

WASN'T IT ASTONISHING HOW IT ALL CAME OUT, THAT ELMER PINCHPENNY WAS THE ONE WHO TRIED TO KILL SANDY?

YES- IT WAS JUST LIKE FATE- IT ALL PROVES WHAT I'VE ALWAYS SAID- THAT THOSE, WHO DO WRONG, ARE ALWAYS PUNISHED, SOONER OR LATER-

2-23-33

MR. AND MRS. FUTILE ARE SURE SWELL FOLKS- MRS. FUTILE IS SURE THE WICKED GET THEIRS- SHE CALLS IT FATE- NO USE O' TELLIN' HER FATE NEEDS A LITTLE HELP, NOW AND THEN-

HELLO, ANNIE- HAVE YOU HEARD ABOUT TH' WRECK? SORTA FUNNY HOW THAT HAPPENED, EH?

YEAH- SEEMS TO ME I HAVE HEARD SOME TALK ABOUT IT- BUT, O' COURSE, ONE CAN HEAR ANYTHING-

HEH-HEH- I USTER THINK I WAS A PRETTY SMART FELLER- BUT I'D SURE HATE TO TRY TO OUT-SMART THAT KID-YES, AND I'D HATE TO HAVE HER OUT AFTER MY HIDE- SHE HASN'T THAT RED HAIR FOR NOTHING-

Reg. U. S. Pat. Off.; Copyright, 1933, by The Chicago Tribune.

HAROLD GRAY

WELL, YOU'VE CERTAINLY MADE A MESS OF THINGS- I HOPE YOU'RE SATISFIED- THAT RED-HEADED LITTLE IMP(AND WHOEVER SHE GOT TO HELP HER) HAVE MADE US THE LAUGHSTOCK OF THIS TOWN-

AW, PIPE DOWN!

2-24-33

WHAT! WHY, YOU IMPUDENT YOUNG PUP- HOW DARE YOU SPEAK TO ME LIKE THAT-

AW, YOU'RE NOT SUCH AN OLD SAINT- HOW DO YOU THINK FOLKS WOULD LIKE TO HEAR ABOUT TH' LAST TIME YOU DROVE A CAR?

IF HE WASN'T MY SON I'D--- I'D- IF HE WERE THE ONLY ONE WHO KNEW--- BUT THAT NEWSPAPER FELLOW, AGATE, AND HIS INSINUATIONS- THAT MIGHT HAVE BEEN A BLUFF-

BUT ONE CAN'T CALL A BLUFF LIKE THAT- WHY, IF IT WERE EVER MADE PUBLIC THAT I WAS THE ONE WHO CRIPPLED PETE PINCHER'S BRAT, I'D BE RUINED- THIS IS INTOLERABLE- THERE MUST BE SOME WAY OUT-

Reg. U. S. Pat. Off.; Copyright, 1933, by The Chicago Tribune.

HAROLD GRAY

IT'S NOT AS THOUGH I HADN'T WARNED ELMER- I TOLD HIM AND TOLD HIM NOT TO RUN OVER ANY MORE DOGS- IF HE'D LISTENED TO ME, HE NEVER WOULD HAVE MADE SUCH A FOOL OF HIMSELF- THE WHOLE TOWN IS LAUGHING-

2-25-33

BUT WHEN I REPRIMAND HIM, HE JEERS AT ME- HE KNOWS I DON'T DARE PUNISH HIM, LEST HE GIVE AWAY THE FACT THAT I STRUCK A CHILD, WITH MY CAR, AND WAS NEVER DETECTED- AR-R-R- THERE'S THAT RED-HEAD-

SHE'S THE ONE THAT'S TO BLAME- I KNOW SHE HAD THAT IRON DOG PLACED BY THE ROADSIDE, EVEN IF I CAN'T PROVE IT- I'LL PAY HER FOR THIS- SHE CAN'T GET AWAY WITH IT-

DON'T LOOK AROUND, SANDY- IT'S OLD PINCHPENNY- HE DOESN'T REALIZE WE CAN SEE HIS REFLECTION, IN THIS SHOW-WINDOW- HM-M-M- WOW- IS HE SORE AT US! GUESS WE'D BETTER KEEP A WEATHER EYE OUT FOR THAT OLD BIRD-

24

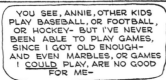

27

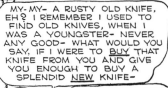

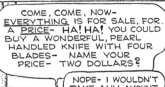

31

32

33

LOOK THERE, AGATE- THERE GOES OLD PINCHPENNY, NOW- I CAN'T FIGURE HIM OUT HERE LATELY-

SH-H- AND THERE'S LITTLE ANNIE- THEY DON'T SEE US- LET'S WATCH THIS MEETING-

3-20-33

YULP!

HELLO, MR. PINCHPENNY- AW, GEE- I DIDN'T MEAN TO S'PRISE YOU-

HA! HA! OH, THAT'S QUITE ALL RIGHT, MY DEAR- QUITE ALL RIGHT- HA! HA!

I JUST GOT WORD FROM TH' MUDDLES AND I KNEW YOU'D BE GLAD TO HEAR HOW WELL THEY'RE GETTIN' ALONG, THANKS TO YOUR HELP-

WHAT DO YOU MAKE OF IT ALL, AGATE? I NEVER SAW SUCH A CHANGE IN ANYONE, IN SUCH A SHORT TIME-

YES- ALL AT ONCE THE OLD HYPOCRITE HAS TURNED SAINT- BUT I'VE NOTICED IT'S ANNIE. WHO SUGGESTS EVERY ONE OF HIS GOOD DEEDS- HM-M- YOU KNOW, DOC, FEAR CAN BE A GREAT WEAPON FOR GOOD, SOMETIMES-

DON'T TRY TO KID ME, YOUNG LADY- WHAT HAVE YOU GOT ON PINCHPENNY? IT MUST BE PLENTY TO TURN THAT OLD MISER INTO A SANTA CLAUS AT YOUR SLIGHTEST SUGGESTION-

HONEST, MR. AGATE- I HAVEN'T A THING ON MR. PINCHPENNY- HE REALLY LIKES TO HELP POOR FOLKS-

3-21-33

YEAH? HE DOES, EH? WELL, IF HE DOES, HE'S SURE CHANGED A LOT ALL OF A SUDDEN- I CAN'T UNDERSTAND IT AT ALL-

I USED TO THINK HE WAS AWFUL TIGHT- BUT NOW HE SPENDS TO HELP ANYBODY, IF I JUST ASK HIM-

THEY CAN SPOUT ABOUT THE POWER OF A SWEET LITTLE CHILD TO REFORM A CROOKED OLD CHISELER LIKE PINCHPENNY- BALONEY- NOT IN THE TWINKLING OF AN EYE, ANYWAY- IT'S SOMETHING ELSE-

LEOPARDS CAN'T CHANGE THEIR SPOTS- STILL, PERHAPS IF A HUMAN LEOPARD WERE SCARED SUFFICIENTLY, HIS SPOTS MIGHT FADE OUT A BIT- FEAR IS THE ONLY POWER THAT COULD MAKE PINCHPENNY REFORM- BUT WHAT IS HE AFRAID OF?

WHAT IF OLD JOHN STUMBLE IS IN NEED? BROUGHT IT ON HIMSELF, DIDN'T HE? WHY DIDN'T HE SAVE HIS MONEY?

THAT'S RIGHT-

YES SIR-

3-22-33

I HAVE NO SYMPATHY FOR SUCH IMPROVIDENT OLD FOOLS- NEVER LOOK AHEAD- NOW HE'S OLD- ALWAYS EXPECT TO BE CARED FOR BY THOSE WHO DID SAVE SOMETHING UP-

YES, MR. PINCHPENNY-

BAH! WHY SHOULD PEOPLE WHO SCRIMP AND SAVE BE EXPECTED TO GIVE THEIR SAVINGS TO THOSE WHO HAVE WASTED EVERY CENT THEY EVER MADE? SUCH WEAKLINGS DON'T DESERVE HELP-

NOPE- YOU'RE RIGHT, THERE-

SUPPOSE WE WERE ALL LIKE OLD JOHN STUMBLE- HUMPH- NO- HE DOESN'T GET A DIME OF MY MONEY- NOT ONE DIME-

I DON'T BLAME YOU, MR. PINCHPENNY-

37

LOOKIE, SANDY— A LOT O' OLD PAPERS IN TH' TOP O' THIS TRUNK— WONDER WHAT THEY ARE—

WHY, HERE'S THAT INSURANCE POLICY, ON TH' HOUSE— YES SIR— THIS IS WHAT MR. FUTILE WAS GOIN' TO LOOK FOR— WAIT A MINUTE— WHY, THIS THING IS NO GOOD, ANY MORE— AT LEAST, I DON'T THINK IT IS—

TH' FUTILES AREN'T HOME— A THING LIKE THIS HADN'T OUGHT TO WAIT— I'M GOIN' TO ASK SOMEBODY WHO KNOWS 'BOUT SUCH THINGS— C'MON, SANDY—

I'M TAKIN' NO CHANCES, AFTER TH' SCARE WE HAD WITH THAT LITTLE FIRE, SATURDAY—

COME IN—

BERT BARRISTER ATTORNEY AT LAW

HAROLD GRAY

4-3-33

MR. PINCHPENNY PROMISED TO HAVE TH' CHURCH PAINTED AND TO PAY FOR A NEW ROOF AND TO BUY A PIPE ORGAN— BUT HE HASN'T DONE ANYTHING ABOUT IT YET—

4-4-33

WONDER WHAT HE'S WAITIN' FOR— HE CAN'T HAVE FORGOTTEN HIS PROMISE— I'VE LOOKED ALL OVER TOWN FOR HIM— WONDER WHERE HE CAN BE—

THAT FIENDISH LITTLE IMP— IS THERE NO WAY TO AVOID HER? I DARE NOT SHOW MYSELF ON THE STREET—

HM-M-M— I'D HAVE SWORN I SAW MR. PINCHPENNY COME THIS WAY— GUESS I'LL SIT DOWN AND WAIT— MAYBE HE'LL SHOW UP—

HAROLD GRAY

4-5-33

OH, GOOD MORNING, MR. PINCHPENNY—

AH, GOOD MORNING, ANNIE— A CHARMING MORNING—

SAY, ABOUT PAINTIN' TH' CHURCH— DON'T YOU THINK THAT OUGHT TO BE DONE, 'FORE THE WEATHER TURNS RAINY, OR SOMETHIN'?

AH- ER- YES- YES- QUITE RIGHT, ANNIE— I'LL ATTEND TO IT AT ONCE— GLAD YOU REMINDED ME—

AH, WHAT I WOULD GIVE TO BE FREE FROM HER ACCURSED POWER— BUT I DARE TAKE NO ONE INTO MY CONFIDENCE— I MUST DO SOMETHING— BUT WHAT?

HAROLD GRAY

42

43

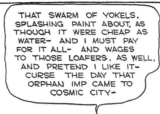

THAT SWARM OF YOKELS, SPLASHING PAINT ABOUT, AS THOUGH IT WERE CHEAP AS WATER– AND I MUST PAY FOR IT ALL– AND WAGES TO THOSE LOAFERS, AS WELL, AND PRETEND I LIKE IT– CURSE THE DAY THAT ORPHAN IMP CAME TO COSMIC CITY–

YES, AND CURSE ME FOR A FOOL THAT NIGHT, FIVE YEARS AGO, THAT I WENT BACK AND LEANED OVER THAT PINCHER BRAT IN THE ROAD, AND LOST MY KNIFE– WHY DIDN'T I DRIVE ON AT ONCE, WITHOUT STOPPING?

BUT THIS OLD INSURANCE POLICY, ON FUTILE'S HOUSE– HE HAS A COPY; BUT, HAD HE SUSPECTED IT HAS EXPIRED, HE MUST HAVE COME TO ME TO HAVE IT RENEWED– NO– HE WOULD NEVER SUSPECT ANYTHING– HM-M-M-----

WELL, THEY'RE COMIN' ALONG GREAT WITH THE PAINTING. DOWN AT THE CHURCH– WONDER IF MR. PINCHPENNY HAS ORDERED THE NEW PIPE ORGAN YET– I'LL HAVE TO REMIND HIM OF THAT–

THAT TROUBLE-MAKING LITTLE SMART ALECK– WELL, SOMETHING TELLS ME SHE WON'T BE IN A POSITION TO DICTATE TO ME MUCH LONGER– THEN LET HER LOOK OUT–

IT'S A TINDER-BOX– AN OLD FIRE-TRAP– A WONDER IT HASN'T BURNED DOWN YEARS AGO– ONCE A FIRE WAS WELL STARTED, THE WHOLE TOWN COULDN'T SAVE EVEN A SHINGLE–

THERE'D BE NO DANGER– THE BEDROOMS ARE ON THE FIRST FLOOR– BUT THERE WOULDN'T BE TIME TO SAVE EVEN CLOTHING– AND THAT KNIFE IN THE ASHES OF A HOUSE– HA! NO ONE WOULD EVER FIND IT, OR RECOGNIZE IT, IF THEY DID–

ELMER IS FOREVER SNOOPING ABOUT AND SPYING ON ME– HE KNOWS TOO MUCH, AS IT IS– HM-M-M– IT WILL BE BETTER TO HAVE HIM OUT OF THE WAY, FOR A FEW DAYS–

AH– PRETTY DULL FOR YOU AROUND HERE, SON– WOULDN'T YOU LIKE TO GO TO THE CITY FOR A LITTLE HOLIDAY? YOU KNOW, ELMER, I WAS YOUNG ONCE MYSELF–

WHAT'S GOT INTO YOU, ALL OF A SUDDEN? WANT TO GET RID OF ME FOR SOME REASON?

HA! HA! YOU KNOW I DON'T, ELMER, MY BOY– I ONLY WANT TO SEE YOU ENJOY YOURSELF– THINK THAT WILL BE ENOUGH?

WELL, I CAN USE THE DOUGH BUT I DON'T GET THE IDEA– STILL, IT'S O.K. WITH ME, I SUPPOSE– HOW MUCH IS THERE HERE?

THE SUSPICIOUS, UNGRATEFUL YOUNG SCOUNDREL– WHAT DID I EVER DO, TO DESERVE SUCH A SON? I'M NOT EASY, WHEN HE'S AROUND–

44

47

Little Orphan Annie

THOSE SHIFTLESS FUTILES AND THAT RED-HEADED IMP- IS THERE NO WAY TO RID THIS TOWN OF THEM? THEY THWART MY EVERY PLAN-

HUMPH- LIVING IN A TENT, LIKE COMMON GYPSIES- THEY'RE A DISGRACE TO COSMIC CITY- IF THAT FIENDISH CHILD HADN'T RENEWED THE INSURANCE, THAT FIRE WOULD HAVE RUINED THEM-

ULP! THAT BRUTE- HE'S MORE WOLF THAN DOG- HOW DID HE KNOW I WAS HERE? I MADE NO SOUND- HE'S A MENACE-

HM-M-M- YOU HAVE A FUNNY LOOK IN YOUR EYE- WHAT HAVE YOU BEEN UP TO NOW? DON'T TRY TO FOOL ME- YOU'RE MIGHTY WELL PLEASED WITH YOURSELF, FOR SOME REASON- I CAN TELL-

OH, NOW I GET IT- OLD PINCHPENNY- LOOK AT HIM GO- I FIGGER YOU CAUGHT THE OLD SNOOPER HANGIN' AROUND HERE AND GAVE HIM A START FOR HOME- IS THAT RIGHT, SANDY?

ARF-

WELL, THEY'RE GETTIN' A PRETTY GOOD START ON TH' NEW HOUSE- GOT TH' FOUNDATIONS ALL REPAIRED AND TH' BASEMENT CLEANED UP THIS PAST WEEK-

AND MOST O TH' LUMBER AND NAILS ARE HERE- THEY'RE GOIN' TO START REALLY BUILDIN' TO-MORROW- IT'LL GO FAST, FROM NOW ON-

A MONTH OR TWO AND WE'LL HAVE A BETTER HOUSE THAN BEFORE- BUT WE'RE SITTIN' PRETTY, IN TH' MEAN TIME- LIVIN' IN A TENT IS SORTA FUN, FOR A CHANGE-

M-M-M- THAT FRIED CHICKEN SMELLS GOOD- IS DINNER ALMOST READY?

ALMOST, ANNIE- IF YOU'LL SET THE TABLE, I'LL BEGIN TAKING THINGS UP-

DID I HEAR SOMEBODY MENTION FRIED CHICKEN?

YEP- AND BISCUITS AND CANDIED SWEET POTATOES- AND WAIT TILL YOU SEE THE PIE-

I DON'T SEE AS CAMPING OUT IS ANY HARDSHIP- I THINK IT'S REAL FUN-

WHOEVER SET FIRE TO OUR HOUSE DID US A FAVOR, WAY IT TURNED OUT- TAKES A GOOD ONE TO GET AHEAD OF A FUTILE-

YEP- IT SURE LOOKS THAT WAY-

HAROLD GRAY

52

54

57

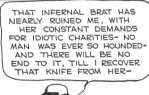

60

62

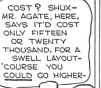

66

Little Orphan Annie

LUCK IS CERTAINLY A FUNNY THING—

FOR INSTANCE— TAKE THIS OLD KNIFE— IT HAPPENED TO FALL INTO THAT CAN O' KEROSENE— AND I JUST HAPPENED TO FIND IT THERE— AND THE KEROSENE TOOK OFF MOST OF TH' RUST AND NOW THE INITIALS ON IT ARE PLAIN AS DAY— P.P.P.— THAT WAS ALL JUST LUCK—

P.P.P.— PHINEAS P. PINCHPENNY— THE KNIFE WAS FOUND FIVE YEARS AGO, RIGHT AT TH' SPOT WHERE POOR LIMPY PINCHER WAS FOUND, AFTER SOME HIT-AND-RUN DRIVER HAD CRIPPLED HIM FOR LIFE— MAYBE THAT WAS JUST LUCK—

MAYBE MR. PINCHPENNY HAD NOTHING TO DO WITH THAT ACCIDENT— MAYBE THIS ISN'T EVEN HIS KNIFE— P.P.P. COULD STAND FOR PLENTY OF OTHER NAMES, AS FAR AS THAT GOES—

IT'D BE AWFUL WRONG TO START TALK 'BOUT A THING LIKE THAT, IF IT ISN'T TRUE— DOESN'T SEEM AS THOUGH A BIG MAN LIKE MR. PINCHPENNY COULD DO A TERRIBLE THING LIKE THAT— I SHOULDN'T THINK SUCH THINGS—

MAYBE MR. PINCHPENNY DIDN'T STOP AND COME BACK TO SEE WHO HE'D HIT, AND LOSE HIS KNIFE— MAYBE MR. PINCHPENNY QUIT DRIVIN' A CAR, JUST AT THAT TIME, JUST BY CHANCE—

AH— THERE SHE IS, ALONE— THE FUTILES ARE AWAY— AND SHE IS LOOKING AT THAT KNIFE— SHE HAS SEEN THE INITIALS— SHE MUST GUESS THE TRUTH—

BUT SHE HASN'T TALKED YET, OR I'D HAVE HEARD OF IT BEFORE THIS— AND SHE MUST NEVER TALK— HOW MY HAND SHAKES——

UH——— WHAT WAS THAT? SOME ONE COMING—— WHAT ACCURSED LUCK—

AH, MR. AGATE— A GLORIOUS DAY FOR A STROLL— DON'T YOU AGREE WITH ME?

YES, INDEED—

NOW, WHAT IS HE UP TO? HE SURE HAD A GUILTY LOOK, IF EVER I SAW ONE—

HELLO, MR. AGATE— COME IN—

FUTILES AWAY EH? DON'T YOU GET AFRAID OUT HERE, ALL ALONE?

SHUX, NO— WHAT IS THERE TO BE SCARED OF AROUND HERE?

HAROLD GRAY

67

68

THERE- THAT JUST ABOUT COVERS IT, I GUESS- I'VE TOLD ALL I KNOW, AND ALL I S'PECT- 'BOUT TH' KNIFE AND WHERE IT WAS FOUND, AND WHEN, AND HOW I FIGGER IT PROVES PINCHPENNY IS TH' BIRD WHO CRIPPLED GUS PINCHER, FIVE YEARS AGO- AND ABOUT HOW FUNNY HE'S ACTED, SINCE I'VE HAD TH' KNIFE-

6-8-33

AND I'VE TOLD 'BOUT THIS BULLET, TOO, AND WHERE I FIGGER IT CAME FROM- NOW I'LL WRAP TH' BULLET AND TH' KNIFE, WITH THIS LETTER, AND SEAL TH' WHOLE PACKAGE, AND PUT IT IN A SAFE PLACE-

I DON'T WANT TO MAKE TROUBLE FOR ANYONE, IF I'M WRONG- BUT IF I'M RIGHT, HE'LL TRY SOMETHIN' ELSE, SOON, WHICH'LL PROVE I'M RIGHT- BUT SUPPOSIN' HE HAD BETTER LUCK, NEXT TIME, THEN THIS PACKET WILL TALK FOR ME-

MR. AGATE WOULD BE TH' MAN TO HANDLE IT- BUT HE'S CURIOUS- HE'D OPEN IT RIGHT AWAY- I DON'T DARE LEAVE IT WITH HIM- NOPE- I'VE GOTTA BE MIGHTY CAREFUL, HOW I HANDLE THIS-

HAROLD GRAY

Reg. U. S. Pat. Off.; Copyright, 1933, by The Chicago Tribune.

SO YOU WANT ME TO KEEP THIS PACKET, IN CASE SOMETHING HAPPENS TO YOU, EH?

YES SIR, MR. BARRISTER- AND IF ANY THING SHOULD HAPPEN TO ME, PLEASE GIVE IT TO MR. AGATE, RIGHT AWAY-

AREN'T YOU BEING A LITTLE THEATRICAL? JUST WHAT DO YOU EXPECT TO HAPPEN TO YOU, ANNIE?

OH, I DON'T KNOW, EXACTLY- THAT'S WHY I WANT TO LEAVE THIS PACKAGE WITH YOU, WHERE IT'LL BE SAFE-

I S'POSE BERT BARRISTER THINKS I'M A SAP- BUT I CAN'T HELP THAT- IF ANYTHING DOES HAPPEN TO ME, HE'LL REMEMBER THAT PACKAGE- IF NOTHIN' HAPPENS, WHAT DIFFERENCE WILL IT MAKE?

SHE'S A FUNNY LITTLE TYKE- AS IF ANYTHING COULD HAPPEN TO HER- SHE MUST HAVE BEEN READING SOME WILD, BLOOD AND THUNDER DETECTIVE STORY- KIDS LIKE MYSTERY- OH, WELL- NO HARM IN KEEPING THE PACKAGE FOR HER-

HAROLD GRAY

Reg. U. S. Pat. Off.; Copyright, 1933, by The Chicago Tribune.

IT'S AWFUL DARK DOWN THAT STREET- SANDY'LL BE ALONG TO MEET ME PRETTY SOON- I'M GOIN' TO WAIT RIGHT HERE, TILL HE COMES- AH, THERE HE IS NOW-

G-10-33

I'M NOT REALLY SCARED- BUT, ON TH' OTHER HAND, WHY TAKE ANY SILLY CHANCES? MOST LIKELY THAT SHOT WAS JUST AN ACCIDENT- NO ONE COULD REALLY WANT TO PLUG ME-

AND, MOST LIKELY, I'VE LET MY 'MAGINATION RUN AWAY WITH ME- MR. PINCHPENNY COULDN'T BE AS BAD, AS I'VE FIGGERED MAYBE HE IS-

JUST TH' SAME- ALL MY FIGGERIN' COMES OUT TOO NEAR EVEN- THERE'S SOMETHIN' FISHY ABOUT THIS WHOLE THING- AND, TILL I FIND OUT JUST WHAT'S WHAT, I'M GOIN' TO BE CAREFUL-

HAROLD GRAY

Reg. U. S. Pat. Off.; Copyright, 1933, by The Chicago Tribune.

WELL, THE NEW HOUSE IS ALMOST FINISHED— THEY SAY WE CAN MOVE IN ON SATURDAY—

6-12-33

THERE'LL BE NO TROUBLE KEEPIN' BUSY THIS WEEK— THE STORE IS GOIN' GREAT— I OUGHT TO BE THERE EVERY MINUTE—

FRIDAY IS TO BE THE LAST DAY OF SCHOOL AND I'VE GOT TO SPEAK A PIECE— I HAVEN'T EVEN STARTED TO LEARN IT YET—

AND SATURDAY WE MOVE INTO TH' NEW HOUSE, AND ALL TH' NEIGHBORS WILL BE THERE, FOR A HOUSE WARMIN'— YEP— THIS IS GOIN' TO BE SOME WEEK—

Reg. U. S. Pat. Off.; Copyright, 1933, by The Chicago Tribune

HAROLD GRAY

I MUST HAVE BEEN GOOFY, TO THINK ANYONE WAS SHOOTIN' AT ME LAST WEEK— DID YOU EVER SEE SUCH A QUIET AND PEACEFUL PLACE, AS COSMIC CITY?

6-13-33

EVERYONE IS FRIENDLY— GUESS I'VE BEEN IMAGINING THINGS— SHUX— WHAT REASON COULD ANYONE HAVE, TO WANT TO HARM ME? I'M TOO SUSPICIOUS—

THAT INFERNAL DOG IS WITH HER, EVERYWHERE SHE GOES— WE MUST SEPARATE THEM—

OH, SHE'LL GO OUT WITHOUT HIM, BEFORE LONG— WE CAN TAKE OUR TIME— THERE'S NO HURRY—

HAROLD GRAY

"NO HURRY!" HUH— WHY, AS LONG AS SHE HAS THAT KNIFE, ANYTHING IS LIABLE TO HAPPEN—

WELL, TAKING THAT SHOT AT HER WAS THE DUMBEST THING YOU COULD HAVE DONE— IT PUT HER ON HER GUARD— NOW WE'VE GOT TO WAIT, TILL SHE GETS CARELESS— THAT'S ALL—

Reg. U. S. Pat. Off.; Copyright, 1933, by The Chicago Tribune.

AW, YOU MAKE ME SICK— THAT OLD KNIFE HAS BECOME AN OBSESSION WITH YOU— FORGET IT, FOR A WHILE—

6-14-33

"FORGET IT!" WHY, YOU YOUNG IDIOT— CAN'T YOU REALIZE, IF THAT KNIFE SHOULD FALL INTO SMART HANDS, IT WOULD BE ENOUGH TO SEND ME TO PRISON?

WELL, WELL, ANNIE— HOW ARE YOU TODAY? ARE YOU GLAD SCHOOL IS NEARLY OVER, FOR THIS YEAR?

HELLO, MR. BARRISTER— OH, I DON'T MIND SCHOOL— BUT VACATION WILL GIVE ME MORE TIME AT THE STORE—

I'M GLAD TO SEE THAT NOTHING HAS HAPPENED TO YOU YET— HA! HA! HA!. ARE YOU STILL FEARING THE WORST?

OH, I GUESS MAYBE THERE WASN'T ANY THING TO BE SCARED OF— BUT YOU KEEP THAT PACKAGE I GAVE YOU, ANY WAY— JUST IN CASE—

Reg. U. S. Pat. Off.; Copyright, 1933, by The Chicago Tribune.

HAROLD GRAY

80

84

86

95

98

103

UGH! THIS IS THEIR CHEAP ROOMING HOUSE— WHAT A LOATHSOME HOVEL— BUT NO DOUBT THEY ARE QUITE COMFORTABLE— IT WOULD NEVER DO TO SPOIL THEM, WITH UN-ACCUSTOMED LUXURY—

FURNISHED ROOMS

8-31-33

MY-MY— WHAT A HOMEY PLACE YOU HAVE HERE— HAVE YOU SEEN THE LOCAL PAPERS? THEY CERTAINLY HAVE GIVEN YOU FOLKS SOME GREAT PUBLICITY—

JUST LOOK AT THESE CLIPPINGS— NOT A KNOCK IN ANY OF THEM— LOOK— HERE'S NEARLY A WHOLE COLUMN— DIDN'T I TELL YOU? JUST KEEP THIS UP AND YOU'LL SOON BE WEARING DIAMONDS—

Reg. U.S. Pat. Off., Copyright, 1933, by The Chicago Tribune

COURSE THOSE WRITE-UPS WERE NICE— BUT YUH CAN'T EAT WRITE-UPS— IF HE WANTS TO BRING US PIECES O' PAPER, I WISH HE'D BRING US TH' KIND WE COULD SPEND—

WHY, ANNIE— WHAT ARE YOU DOING OUT IN FRONT HERE?

9-1-33

OH, I WAS JUST SORT O' COUNTIN' TH' FOLKS, AS THEY GO IN— GEE— THERE'S A LONG LINE WAITIN'— THIS WEEK WE OUGHT TO MAKE A LOT O' MONEY— HOW MUCH DO WE GET ON EACH ONE?

HO! HO! NOW DON'T YOU WORRY YOUR PRETTY HEAD OVER SUCH THINGS— YOU JUST LEAVE ALL THOSE BOTHERSOME BUSINESS MATTERS TO OLD C.C.— WHY, THAT'S WHAT I'M FOR— TO SEE THAT YOU GET WHAT'S DUE YOU—

THAT BRAT IS TOO NOSEY— I'VE GOT TO KEEP AN EYE ON HER EVERY MINUTE— KEEP 'EM DUMB— THAT'S THE ONLY WAY TO HANDLE 'EM—

STAGE ENTRANCE

HAROLD GRAY

Reg. U.S. Pat. Off., Copyright, 1933, by The Chicago Tribune

WELL-WELL— PAY DAY AGAIN— MONEY- MONEY- MONEY- YOU'RE A HEAP BETTER OFF THAN LOTS OF PEOPLE, THESE DAYS—

HOW MUCH BETTER OFF? WITH THE CROWDS WE'VE HAD AT THE THEATRE, WE SHOULD HAVE MADE A LOT—

9-2-33

TWELVE DOLLARS EVEN— NOT BAD, EH?

TWELVE DOLLARS! PHOOIE! WHY, WE MADE MORE THAN THAT IN ONE DAY, PLENTY O' DAYS, BEFORE WE MET YOU— TWELVE DOLLARS!

BUT YOU CAN'T EXPECT A FORTUNE OVER NIGHT— LAST WEEK IT WAS ONLY $11.20— GREAT SCOTT! I'M DOING ALL I CAN— THINK OF THE FUTURE—

Reg. U.S. Pat. Off., Copyright, 1933, by The Chicago Tribune

YEAH— I AM— AND IF TH' FUTURE IS GOIN' TO BE ANYTHING LIKE THIS, I WOULDN'T CARE FOR ANY— TWELVE BUCKS FOR A WHOLE WEEK'S WORK, FOR TH' TWO OF US— BAH!

HAROLD GRAY

109

I SAW YOU COLLECT FROM THE THEATRE MANAGER- HE PAID YOU HUNDREDS- AND YOU TRY TO TELL US OUR SHARE IS ONLY A MEASLY TWENTY-ONE BUCKS- YOU MUST THINK WE'RE CRAZY-

WHY, ANNIE- YOU'RE TERRIBLY MISTAKEN- YOU DO ME A GRAVE INJUSTICE- TWENTY-ONE DOLLARS WAS YOUR FULL SHARE- YOU COULDN'T HAVE SEEN ANY SUCH AMOUNT. AS YOU CLAIM- IT'S PREPOSTEROUS- DON'T YOU TRUST ME?

WHY, THE WEEK BEFORE IT WAS ONLY $12- THIS WEEK IT WAS $21- WHY, THAT'S AN INCREASE OF 75%- THINK OF IT- AT THAT RATE YOU'LL SOON BE MAKING THOUSANDS- ONLY HAVE FAITH IN ME, AND YOU'LL BE RICH SO SOON IT WILL MAKE YOUR HEAD SWIM- AW, NOW- DON'T MAKE ME CRY-

9-11

HOW IN THE WORLD DID SHE SEE ME GET THAT MONEY- I CERTAINLY PULLED A DUMB ONE- SHE'LL NEVER FORGET IT- WELL, ONE THING SURE- I'LL SEE TO IT SHE NEVER GETS ANYTHING ON ME AGAIN- THE NOSEY LITTLE BRAT-

Reg. U. S. Pat. Off.; Copyright, 1933, by The Chicago Tribune

HAROLD GRAY

BUT I TELL YOU, I SAW HIM GET THE MONEY- THERE WERE HUNDREDS- THERE WAS ONE BIG BUNDLE, ALL TWENTIES, AND A LOT BESIDES- AND HE GAVE US ONLY TWENTY-ONE BUCKS-

9-12-33

BUT THE CONTRACT, ANNIE- HE COULDN'T DO A THING LIKE THAT- HE IS TO GET HALF AND WE ARE TO GET HALF- THAT WAS IN THE CONTRACT-

THAT'S JUST IT- HE CAN'T CHEAT US, BUT HE IS CHEATIN' US, JUST THE SAME- I TELL YOU THAT BIRD IS JUST A CHEAP CROOK-

Reg. U. S. Pat. Off. Copyright, 1933, by The Chicago Tribune

OH, ANNIE- YOU MUST BE MISTAKEN- NOT MR. CHIZZLER- THERE MUST BE SOME BIG MISTAKE SOME WHERE-

I'LL SAY THERE'S A MISTAKE- OUR MEETIN' HIM WAS IT-

HAROLD GRAY

THERE GOES MR. CHIZZLER- SO THAT'S WHERE HE'S STAYING, WHILE WE'RE IN THIS TOWN- THE SWELLEST HOTEL-

9-13-33

I KNOW WHAT GOOD HOTELS COST- HE MUST SPEND MORE THERE, IN A DAY, THAN WE DO IN A WEEK- AND HE'S BOUGHT SOME SWELL NEW CLOTHES LATELY, AND LOTS O' NEW THINGS-

AND 'TH' BEST WE CAN AFFORD IS A DIRTY LITTLE ROOM, UP THREE FLIGHTS, AND EATS FROM A DELICATESSEN- MOST ALL WE GET GOES FOR CAR-FARE-

FURNISHED ROOMS

Reg. U. S. Pat. Off. Copyright, 1933, by The Chicago Tribune

OUR CONTRACT SAYS WE'RE TO GET TH' SAME AS HE GETS- HE CAN'T LIVE, TH' WAY HE LIVES ON ANY $21 A WEEK- NO SIR- WE'RE GETTING A PHONEY DEAL- THAT'S SURE-

HAROLD GRAY

119

125

126

Little Orphan Annie

OW! MY THROAT!

GEE, "UNCLE" DAN- IF WE COULD ONLY GET OUT OF THIS DAMP, DARK, OLD ROOM, I THINK I'D FEEL BETTER-

BUT WE HAVEN'T ANY MONEY, ANNIE- WE EVEN OWE FOR A WEEK'S RENT HERE- MR. CHIZZLER HASN'T PAID US FOR THE WEEK BEFORE LAST-

I GUESS HE WOULD HAVE PAID US LAST SUNDAY, BUT I GOT SICK, AND HE FORGOT IT- DIDN'T HE SAY HE WAS COMING TO SEE ME?

YES- HE SAID HE WAS GOING TO BRING A DOCTOR- THEY OUGHT TO BE HERE ANY MOMENT-

MY THROAT HURTS AWFUL- AND IT'S GETTIN' WORSE- WHY DON'T THEY COME?

SH! THAT'S MR. CHIZZLER'S STEP, IN THE HALL- AND SOME ONE IS WITH HIM-

HERE WE ARE, DOCTOR- I DON'T IMAGINE IT'S ANYTHING SERIOUS- JUST A LITTLE COLD. NO DOUBT-

AH- SO THIS IS OUR PATIENT, EH?

I KEEP TELLING HER SHE COULD SING, IF SHE WASN'T SUCH A BABY-

HM-M- NOT SO GOOD-

WELL, LITTLE LADY, YOU HAVE A PRETTY BAD THROAT THERE- YOU'LL NOT SING AGAIN; FOR A LONG TIME, AT LEAST- BUT I'LL GIVE MR. CHIZZLER A PRESCRIPTION FOR YOU, AND HE MUST GET YOU OUT OF THIS PLACE-

SHE'LL NOT SING FOR A YEAR AT LEAST- FILL THIS PRESCRIPTION AT ONCE AND GIVE IT TO HER, TO RELIEVE THE PAIN- AND GET HER TO A HOSPITAL-

YES, YES, DOCTOR- MY-MY- I HAD NO IDEA SHE WAS SO SICK-

BAH! SHE'S NO MORE GOOD TO ME- WHY WASTE MONEY ON MEDICINE FOR HER? I'LL CALL THAT DOC. LATER AND TELL HIM THEY HAVE RUN OUT ON ME- THAT WILL KEEP HIM FROM CHECKING UP ON THE CASE-

AND I'LL CHECK OUT OF THIS HOTEL IN A HURRY, SO THE DOC OR THAT BRAT CAN'T FIND ME- LUCKY I DIDN'T PAY THEM LAST WEEK- I SAVED THAT MUCH, AT LEAST-

AH- SAFE IN A TAXI- GREAT SCOTT- SHE WOULD LOSE HER VOICE, JUST AS I WAS SET TO MAKE A FORTUNE- WHAT DID I EVER DO TO DESERVE SUCH LUCK?

WHY ISN'T HE BACK? YOU DON'T SUPPOSE HE'S RUN OUT ON US, DO YOU, "UNCLE" DAN?

OH, HE'LL HAVE TO COME BACK, TO PAY US FOR THE LAST WEEK WE WORKED- HE COULDN'T BE SO INHUMAN AS TO LEAVE US THIS WAY-

127

THAT DOC., OR ANNIE, WILL NEVER FIND ME, SINCE I MOVED TO THIS HOTEL- BUT I'LL STAY IN TOWN AND KEEP AN EYE ON THAT KID- SHE MIGHT GET WELL- IF SO, I CAN RE-APPEAR-

10-23-33

THAT DOC. GAVE ME A PRESCRIPTION TO FILL FOR HER AND TOLD ME TO GET HER TO A HOSPITAL- BAH- WHY WASTE MONEY ON HER- BUT I MUST KEEP THE DOC. FROM CHECKING UP ON THE CASE-

YES, DOCTOR- I JUST CALLED TO TELL YOU THE LITTLE GIRL WAS GONE, WHEN I GOT BACK- YES- RAN AWAY- NO TELLING WHERE- YES, IT IS TOO BAD- BUT WE DID OUR BEST, EH?

BUT WHY DID MR. CHIZZLER DESERT US? WHY ARE YOU LAUGHING, ANNIE?

HA! HA! JUST THINKIN'- WITH CHIZZLER STEALIN' MOST ALL WE MADE, THINK HOW MUCH MORE HE'S LOSIN' NOW, THAN WE'RE LOSIN'- HA! HA! HA!

HAROLD GRAY

Reg. U.S. Pat. Off.; Copyright, 1933 by The Chicago Tribune

TAKE IT EASY, DRIVER- AH- THERE'S THE FILTHY HOVEL, WHERE THEY HAVE THEIR ROOM- AND THERE'S OLD BALLAD, DODDERING INTO THE PLACE, WITH THE DOG LEADING HIM-

10-24-33

THAT'S ALL I WANTED TO KNOW- THEY'RE STILL THERE- IF THE BRAT GETS HER VOICE BACK, SHE'S STILL MY TRAINED SEAL- IF NOT, I'LL STAY OUT OF THE PICTURE-

WHERE DID YOU GO, "UNCLE" DAN?

TO THE DELICATESSEN- BUT WE HAVE SO LITTLE MONEY- AND PRICES ARE SO HIGH- I COULD BUY VERY LITTLE-

DON'T YOU WORRY ABOUT ME- I'M NOT VERY HUNGRY, ANYWAY-

I NEVER THOUGHT MR. CHIZZLER COULD BE SO CRUEL, AS TO DESERT US, AT SUCH A TIME-

HAROLD GRAY

Reg. U.S. Pat. Off.; Copyright, 1933 by The Chicago Tribune

WELL, IF WE CAN'T PAY OUR RENT, WE JUST CAN'T- THAT'S ALL-

YES- BUT THE LANDLORD WAS VERY UNPLEASANT TO ME, AS I CAME IN JUST NOW-

10-25-33

THAT BRAT'S GOT SOMETHIN'- NO TELLIN' WHAT- LIKE AS NOT SHE'LL GET MY PLACE HERE QUARANTINED, YET- MAYBE SCARE 'EM, THEY PAY UP-

WHAT ABOUT MY RENT, HEY? YOU THINK I RUN A FREE HOTEL HERE, MAYBE- YOU PAY UP BY SUNDAY, OR OUT YOU GO, ON YOUR EAR- SEE?

AW, DON'T TAKE IT SO HARD- WE'VE GOT TILL SUNDAY- WHY LOOK AHEAD FOR SOMETHIN' TO WORRY ABOUT?

BUT I CAN SEE NO WAY OUT, ANNIE- AND YOU MUST HAVE A DOCTOR, FOR YOUR THROAT-

HAROLD GRAY

Reg. U.S. Pat. Off.; Copyright, 1933 by The Chicago Tribune

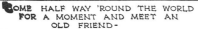

I'VE GOT TO RAISE FIVE HUNDRED DOLLARS- FOR THIRTY FIVE HUNDRED, THAT FOOL, MORENO PALMETTO, WILL SELL ME THOSE STOLEN CROWN JEWELS-

I'VE GOT THREE THOUSAND, I MADE OFF OF THAT BRAT, BEFORE SHE LOST HER VOICE- ALL I NEED IS ANOTHER FIVE HUNDRED- THEN TO GET THOSE JEWELS, AND MILLIONS-

THE MANAGER? OH, YES- HA! HA! A WEEK BEHIND IN MY ROOM RENT? TCH! TCH! I'LL TAKE CARE OF IT TO-MORROW- OH, ABSOLUTELY- YOU CAN COUNT ON IT-

HAH- ONCE I GET THOSE JEWELS, I CAN BUY THIS HOTEL- I'LL PAWN EVERYTHING- SUITS- WATCH- OVERCOAT- CANE- SHIRTS- WHAT'S THE DIFFERENCE? I'LL REDEEM THEM, IN A COUPLE OF DAYS-

I'VE PAWNED EVERY THING I OWN, EXCEPT THE CLOTHES I STAND IN- BUT WHAT OF IT? A FEW MORE MINUTES AND I'LL BE RICH, BEYOND MY WILDEST DREAMS- AH- HERE COMES THAT FOREIGNER, NOW-

11-7-33

THERE WE ARE- THIRTY FIVE HUNDRED DOLLARS- AH- I SEE YOU BROUGHT THE JEWELS-

I SHQULD NOT DO THEES THING- EET IS WRONG I SHOULD PART WITH ZE CROWN JEWELS OF MY BELOVED COUNTRY, BUT I AM HELP- LESS-

OH! BABY! JUST LOOK AT 'EM SHINE! DIAMONDS- RUBIES- EMERALDS- AND A LOT I DON'T KNOW WHAT TO CALL- I'VE DONE IT AT LAST- I'M RICH!

WELL, CHIZZLER, OLD KID- THE WISE GUY, EH? THE ORPHAN ROBBER- THE BIRD WHO STEALS FROM BLIND MEN- WHAT A HEAD-ACHE HE'S IN FOR- WELL, HE ASKED FOR IT-

NOT WORTH FIVE DOLLARS! WHY, THEY'RE WORTH MILLIONS! THEY'RE CROWN JEWELS, I TELL YOU- AND YOU SAY THEY'RE WORTHLESS-

VERY SORRY, SIR-

11-8-33

TAKE IT EASY, BUD!

YOU CAN'T DO THIS TO ME-

AH, DON'T FORGET YOUR PARCEL, SIR-

HE MUST BE CRAZY-

NUTTY AS A SQUIRREL- HEY, COLUMBUS- DON'T FORGET THEM CROWN JEWELS- WHAT'D QUEEN ISABELLA SAY?

ME- THROWN OUT INTO THE ALLEY-

I WAS SO SURE THEY WERE REAL- WHAT CAN I DO? I'VE PAWNED EVERY THING- I HAVEN'T A CENT- I CAN'T GO BACK TO THE HOTEL- OH, WHAT DID I EVER DO TO DESERVE THIS?

136

137

138

139

142

143

144

145

146

149

I HAD TO COME WAY OVER HERE, TO TH' OTHER SIDE O' TOWN, BUT IT WAS WORTH IT— I GAVE THOSE OLD TROUBLE-MAKERS TH' SLIP, THIS TIME—

12-14-33

AND I GOT A GOOD JOB, IN THIS LITTLE STORE—THE BOSS THINKS I LIVE NEAR HERE— I DO— BUT HE DOESN'T KNOW I LIVE IN A PIANO BOX, IN TH' ALLEY—

HE'D HAVE A FIT, IF HE KNEW HE'D HIRED AN ORPHAN, MOST LIKELY— BUT WHAT HE DOESN'T KNOW, CAN'T HURT ME, I FIGGER—

HAROLD GRAY

Reg. U. S. Pat. Off.; Copyright, 1933, by The Chicago Tribune.

AT HONOLULU, ALMOST READY TO HOP OFF—

YOU'RE TAKING A MIGHTY LONG CHANCE, MR. WARBUCKS—

POPPYCOCK— IF YOU'RE SCARED, I'LL GET ANOTHER PILOT— OR, FAILING THAT, I'LL 'SOLO—

THERE SHE IS— GRAB HER—

WE'LL PROSECUTE YOU— SHE'S A MINOR AND AN ORPHAN— STOP HER, I SAY—

12-15-33

STOP HER—

THAT'S TH' CHRISTMAS SPIRIT— A GOOD DEED EVERY DAY, EH? PHOOIE!

IT MUST FEEL WONDERFUL TO KNOW YOU'RE SO DOG-GONED GOOD— WELL, GIVE ME FOLKS WITH LESS GOODNESS AND MORE KINDNESS—

OFF FROM HONOLULU——— WHAT WILL "DADDY'S" NEXT STOP BE? THE MAINLAND OF NORTH AMERICA OR A WATERY GRAVE?

HAROLD GRAY

Reg. U. S. Pat. Off.; Copyright, 1933, by The Chicago Tribune.

THERE TH' TWO OLD BUZZARDS ARE, PROWLIN' UP AND DOWN, IN FRONT O' TH' STORE, HOPIN' I'LL COME BACK— WHY CAN'T THEY FALL INTO A COAL HOLE, OR HAVE A SAFE FALL ON 'EM?

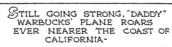

STILL GOING STRONG, "DADDY" WARBUCKS' PLANE ROARS EVER NEARER THE COAST OF CALIFORNIA—

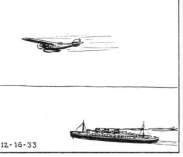

12-16-33

UP TO TEN THOUSAND FEET, WHILE FAR BELOW, THE SEA IS BLOTTED OUT BY THE THRESHING MONSTER OF A TERRIFIC STORM—

THE WEATHER IS CLEARING— IT WILL BE SUN DOWN IN TWENTY MINUTES—

YES— AND LOOK— SEE THAT BLUE LINE? THAT'S CALIFORNIA— WE'RE GOING TO MAKE IT—

HAROLD GRAY

Reg. U. S. Pat. Off.; Copyright, 1933, by The Chicago Tribune.

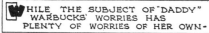

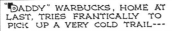

154

155

DO YOU REALIZE, SANDY, "DADDY" HASN'T SAID A WORD ABOUT TRIXIE? WHERE IS SHE? WHAT'S BECOME OF HER? MAYBE HE'S JUST FORGOTTEN TO TELL US—

12-28-33

YOU'VE TOLD US HARDLY A THING ABOUT YOUR TRIP, "DADDY"—

NOT MUCH TO TELL, ANNIE— HAD A LOT OF BAD WEATHER— A TYPHOON CAUGHT US AND THE SHIP NEARLY SANK—

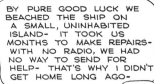

BY PURE GOOD LUCK WE BEACHED THE SHIP ON A SMALL, UNINHABITED ISLAND— IT TOOK US MONTHS TO MAKE REPAIRS— WITH NO RADIO, WE HAD NO WAY TO SEND FOR HELP— THAT'S WHY I DIDN'T GET HOME LONG AGO—

GEE—

WELL, IF HE'D WANTED TO TELL US ABOUT TRIXIE, I GUESS HE'D HAVE TOLD US— HE SURE KNEW HE WAS BEIN' ASKED—

HAROLD GRAY
Reg. U. S. Pat. Off.; Copyright, 1933, by The Chicago Tribune.

OF COURSE EVERYONE WANTS TO KNOW WHAT HAS BECOME OF TRIXIE— AS YET NO ONE HAS COME RIGHT OUT AND ASKED— I COULD TELL MY FRIENDS THE WHOLE STORY— BUT I'M NOT GOING TO— NOT NOW, AT ANY RATE—

12-29-33

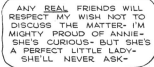

ANY REAL FRIENDS WILL RESPECT MY WISH NOT TO DISCUSS THE MATTER— I'M MIGHTY PROUD OF ANNIE— SHE'S CURIOUS— BUT SHE'S A PERFECT LITTLE LADY— SHE'LL NEVER ASK—

WUN WEY, TOO, IS CURIOUS— WE FIND HIM ALONE, WITH HIS THOUGHTS—

ONE DOES NOT ASK SUCH A QUESTION OF A FRIEND, OR DOES ONE ATTEMPT TO PEER BEHIND THE VEIL— IN TIME, IF ONE IS PATIENT, ALL KNOWLEDGE COMES TO ONE—

GOOD OLD JAKE, IN HIS PRIVATE OFFICE AT HIS STORE, PONDERS THE MATTER—

FROM SUCH A MAN I WOULD NOT ASK— IT IS A FINE THING EVERY MAN MINDS HIS OWN BUSINESS— IT IS A FINE THING FOR THE BUSINESS, TOO —-YES—

HAROLD GRAY
Reg. U. S. Pat. Off.; Copyright, 1933, by The Chicago Tribune.

WELL, SANDY— ANOTHER YEAR ALMOST GONE— IT'S BEEN PLENTY TOUGH IN SPOTS, TOO— COURSE WE GOT ALONG GREAT AT TH' FUTILE'S—

12-30-33

THAT IS WE DID, TILL WE GOT JAMMED UP WITH OLD PINCHPENNY AND HIS MEAN SON, ELMER— THEY MIGHTY NEAR FINISHED US, A COUPLE O' TIMES—

AND THERE WAS THE TOUGH SLEDDING, WHEN CHIZZLER ROBBED US BLIND— BUT PINCHPENNYS GOT THEIRS— AND WE GOT SHUT O' CHIZZLER— AND WHEN THINGS LOOKED ALMOST WORSE'N EVER "DADDY" CAME BACK—

WELL, NO MATTER HOW TOUGH SOME OF THE SPOTS WERE, DURIN' 1933, TH' ENDIN' WAS O.K., EH, SANDY?

ARF—

HAROLD GRAY
Reg. U. S. P... Off.; Copyright, 1933...

156